Better Vocals W.

Rockschool

A *Rockschool* Publication
www.rockschool.co.uk

Welcome To Level 3 *Male Vocals*

Welcome to the Rockschool Level 3 candidate pack for Male Vocals. This pack includes all the prepared elements needed by a candidate to take grades 6, 7 and 8. In the book you will find exam scores for the performance pieces consisting of a vocal line and chord boxes.

The CDs have backing tracks for the technical exercises and backing tracks for each song. Examples of all the other tests contained in the exam are contained in the *Companion Guide* accompanying this series.

If you have any queries about this or any other Rockschool exam, please call us on **020 8332 6303** or email us at office@rockschool.co.uk. Visit our website http://www.rockschool.co.uk. Good luck!

Grade 6

Pieces at this level will be more complex in construction and content and will require a more solid understanding of stylistic matters. The candidate will require knowledge of suitable tone, delivery and rhythm and be expected to portray the song with increasing confidence. The candidate is also expected to demonstrate increasing knowledge of microphone techniques. The candidate will be expected to be able to move effortlessly between registers and to have a wide range of dynamic control and articulation. **All pieces are to be memorised to enable the candidate to gain an increasing sense of performance. A microphone must be used throughout the exam.**

Grade 7

At this level pieces will be of a substantial length to enable the candidate to demonstrate a thorough working knowledge of suitable stylistic techniques. The pieces will require considerable personal interpretation, with improvisation and ornamentation used to produce a balanced musical result. The candidate is expected to perform the pieces with a considerable sense of commitment and musical integrity and with a well grounded sense of performance and communication. **All pieces are to be memorised to enable the candidate to gain an increasing sense of performance. A microphone must be used throughout the exam.**

Grade 8

At this level the main emphasis is on performance and this is demonstrated in a complete control of suitable stylistic techniques. The candidate is expected to make full use of microphone techniques to enhance their performance and to demonstrate a secure ability in register and tone. Considerable improvisation and ornamentation is expected to produce an advanced and mature sense of performance with a high degree of personal interpretation. **All pieces are to be memorised to enable the candidate to gain an increasing sense of performance. A microphone must be used throughout the exam.**

How To Use The CD

The Level 3 book contains two CDs. On these you will find the backing tracks to the exercises and the songs. You should prepare the exercises and the songs using these CDs to perform with in the exam.

For the scales in grades 6, 7 and 8, the first backing track is in the key of A. You will find alternative keys for the scales at the end of the CD in all keys between B♭ and D around middle C. Any of these keys can be used in the exam.

Important Information For Candidates

Candidates may use this syllabus to enter for either a **grade exam** or a **performance certificate** at grades 6, 7 or 8. If you are entering for a **grade exam**, you will need to prepare the following elements. You will perform them in the exam in the order in which they are shown below. Full syllabus requirements can be found in the *Rockschool Vocal Syllabus Guide* which can be downloaded from www.rockschool.co.uk.

Technical exercises (10 marks). You will find two sets of exercises printed for each grade: a scale test and backing tracks exercise.

General Musicianship Questions (5 marks). You will be asked five questions at the end of the exam. Three of these will refer to the pieces. You will be asked questions on note values, dynamic markings, articulation markings, key and time signatures and general musical directions. One question will be asked about general vocal technique and a final question on performance and interpretation. Please refer to the *Syllabus Guide* for the GMQ requirements.

Quick Study Piece (15 marks). You will be asked to prepare and perform a Quick Study Piece (QSP) in the exam. You should arrive at the exam centre half an hour before your due examination time and you will be given the QSP to practice 20 minutes in advance of entering the exam room. Please refer to the *Syllabus Guide* for the QSP requirements. Examples are printed in the *Companion Guide*.

Aural Tests (10 marks). There are two aural tests in each grade. Examples are printed in the *Companion Guide*. The requirements for each grade are as follows:

• **Grade 6**. You will be given a four bar melodic phrase made up of notes and rests. You will also be given a set of rhythmic examples. One of these corresponds to the rests in the melodic phrase. You will select the appropriate test and you will be asked to clap the rest rhythm. The rests will fall on the beat and consist of quaver and crotchet note values. Next you will be given a simple four bar phrase with chord symbols. You will be asked harmonise a simple line after hearing the test three times.

• **Grade 7**. As for Grade 6 but with more complex rhythmic patterns. The rests will fall on and off the beat and consist of quaver and crotchet note values. There will be some note values combined into rests. (2 semiquavers = 1 quaver rest). The 2nd test will be a chord chart. You will hear the complete test once and will be required to sing the bass progression, including 1st inversions, on the repeat. **This test is continuous.**

• **Grade 8**. You will hear an eight bar melody in major or natural minor twice, and will be asked to harmonise a moving line on the 3rd hearing. The 2nd test will be a chord chart in a rhythm. You will hear the complete test once and will be required to sing the bass progression including 1st inversions, on the repeat. **This test is continuous.**

Three performance pieces (60 marks). You are not limited solely to the songs printed in this book. You may perform **either** three songs from this book (including one or more from the supplementary list printed for each grade), **or** you may bring in **one** song not included in these lists to perform in the exam. This may be a hit from the chart or a song of your own composing. Please ensure, though, that you have the appropriate backing track. Please turn to the Guru's Guide on page 62 for the list of supplementary material.

If you are entering a **performance certificate**, you will perform five songs, of which up to two may be from repertoire not included in this book or the companion Level 3 volume.

The Level 3 *Male Vocals* book is a companion to the Level 3 *Female Vocals* book. Candidates are welcome to perform repertoire contained in either book in the exam of equivalent difficulty.

Grade 6 *Technical Exercises*

In this section, the examiner will ask you to perform the two exercises printed below. You do not need to memorise the exercises (and you may use the book in the exam) but the examiner will be looking for the speed and confidence of your response. The examiner will also give you credit for the level of your musicality in your attention to directions, including phrasing and dynamics.

Exercise 1: Scales Disc 1 Track 1

You will be asked to perform the following scale and arpeggio exercise beginning on any note between **A-D**. You will be asked to give the exercise *legato* or *staccato* and with *crescendo* and *diminuendo* as directed by the examiner.

Exercise 2: Backing Vocals

You should prepare all three parts of the following two backing vocal exercises. The examiner will select the part to be given against the other two parts on a backing track. Two examples to be selected.

Exercise 3: Backing Vocals (continued)

Disc 1 Track 5/6/7

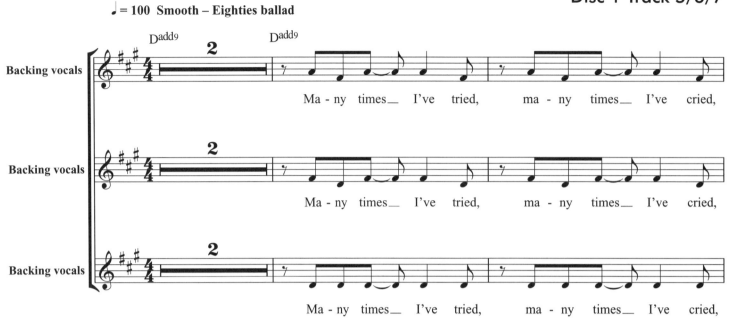

Ma - ny times__ I've tried, ma - ny times__ I've cried,

Ma - ny times__ I've tried, ma - ny times__ I've cried,

Ma - ny times__ I've tried, ma - ny times__ I've cried,

ma - ny times____ you've lied, ma - ny times____ I've tried.

ma - ny times____ you've lied, ma - ny times____ I've tried.

ma - ny times____ you've lied, ma - ny times____ I've tried.

The Boys Are Back In Town

Words & Music by Phil Lynott

Vocals Level 3 - Male

Can't Buy Me Love

Words & Music by
John Lennon & Paul McCartney

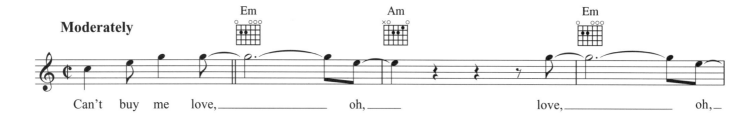

Can't buy me love, _____ oh, ____ love, _____ oh, __

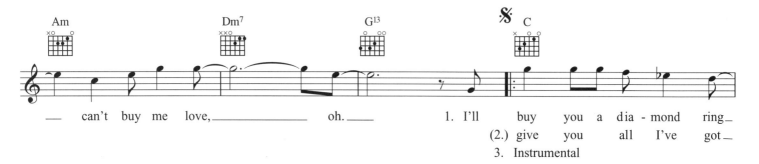

__ can't buy me love, _____ oh. ____

1. I'll buy you a dia-mond ring
(2.) give you all I've got __
3. Instrumental

__ my friend __ if it makes you feel all right. ____ I'll get you an-y-thing, __
__ to give __ if you say you love me too. ____ I may not have a lot __

__ my friend, __ if it makes you feel al-right. ____ 'Cause
__ to give, __ But what I've got I'll give to you. ____ For } I don't care too

much for mon-ey, for mon-ey can't buy me love. ____ 2. I'll __ Can't buy me love __

_____ oh, ____ ev-'ry-bod-y tells me so. ____ Can't buy me love __

Vocals Level 3 - Male

Brand New Day

Words & Music by Sting

Intro

New tempo

Verse

1. How man-y of you peo-ple___ out there___ been hurt   in some kind of love af-fair   and
2. Love   is pain   I hear you say,   love has a cruel   and bit-ter way of pay-ing you

how man-y times did you___ swear that you'd nev-er   love a-gain?___
back   for all   the faith you ev-er had   in your   brain.

How man-y lone-ly, sleep-less nights, how man-y lies,   how man-y fights?___ And why
How could it be that what you need the most   can leave you feel-ing just like a ghost,   you

would you want to   put your-self___ through all   of that a-gain?
nev-er want to   feel so sad   and lost   a-gain.

One day you could be look - ing through an old book in rain - y weath - er, you see a

pic - ture of her smil - ing at you when you were still to - geth - er. You could be

walk - ing down the street and who should you choose to meet, but that

same old smile you've been think - in' of all day, mm. Why don't we

Chorus

turn the clock to ze - ro hon - ey, I'll sell the stock, we'll spend all the mon - ey, we're
turn the clock to ze - ro hon - ey, I'll sell the stock, we'll spend all the mon - ey, we're

start - ing up a brand new day. Turn the clock all the way back, I'll
start - ing up a brand new day. Turn the clock to zero and back, I'm

won - der, if she'll take me back, I'm think - ing in a brand new way.
beg - gin' her to take me back, I'm think - ing in a brand new way.

Outro Choruses:

4. Stand up all you lovers in the world
    Stand up and be counted, every boy and every girl
    Stand up all you lovers in the world
    We're starting up a brand new day.

5. You're the crop to my rotation
    You're the sum of my equation
    I'm the answer to your question
    If you follow my suggestion.

6. We can turn this ship around
    We'll go up instead of down
    You're the pan and I'm the handle
    You're the flame and I'm the candle.

7. *As Chorus 4*

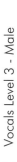

Summer Of '69

Words & Music by
Bryan Adams & Jim Vallance

Intro D⁵ **Verse**

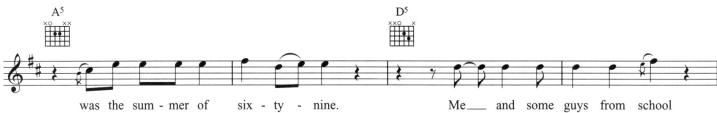

_mf_

1. I got my first real six string,—

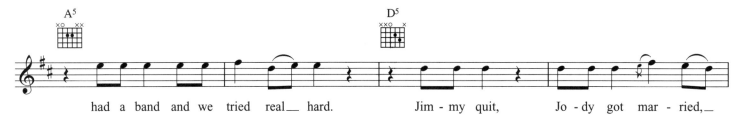

bought_ it at the five and_ dime, played it un-til my fin-gers_ bled,

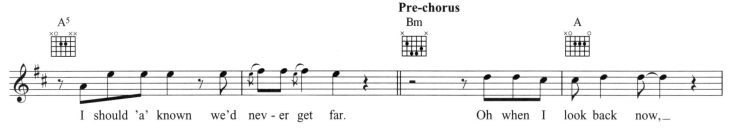

was the sum-mer of six-ty-nine. Me_ and some guys from school

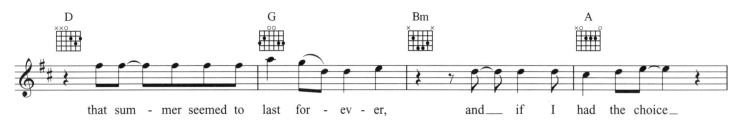

had a band and we tried real_ hard. Jim-my quit, Jo-dy got mar-ried,—

Pre-chorus

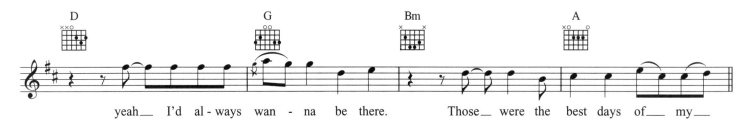

I should 'a' known we'd nev-er get far. Oh when I look back now,—

that sum-mer seemed to last for-ev-er, and_ if I had the choice_

yeah_ I'd al-ways wan-na be there. Those_ were the best days of_ my

Babylon

Words & Music by
David Gray

♩ = 112

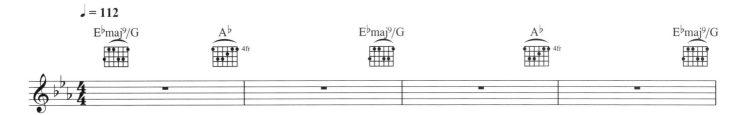

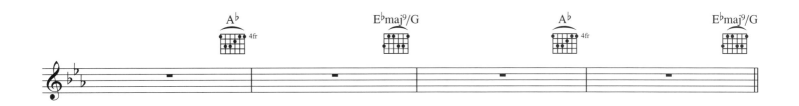

1. Fri - day night,_ an' I'm go - in' no - where; all the lights_ are chang - in' green_ to red._

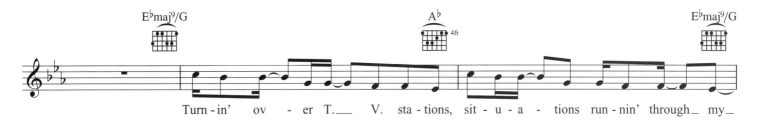

Turn - in' ov - er T._ V. sta - tions, sit - u - a - tions run - nin' through_ my_

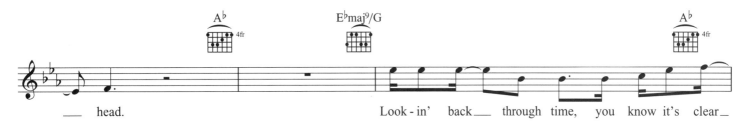

_ head. Look - in' back_ through time, you know it's clear_

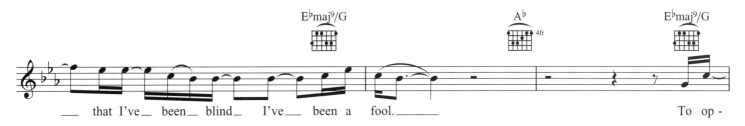

_ that I've_ been_ blind_ I've_ been a fool._ To op -

- en up_ my heart_ to all_ that jea - lous - y,_ that bit - ter - ness,_ that_ ri - di - cule.

Vocals Level 3 - Male

Fm Gm11 E♭ B♭
for cry - in' out loud. The love that I was giv - in' you was
Fm A♭ E♭ B♭
never in doubt. Let go your heart, let go your head
Fm B♭ E♭ B♭ Fm
To Coda
and feel it now. Let go your heart, let go your head, and feel it
1. B♭ E♭maj9/G A♭ E♭maj9/G A♭
now, Ba - by - lon, Ba - by - lon,
E♭maj9/G A♭ E♭maj9/G A♭ E♭maj9/G
2. B♭
D.S. al Coda
Ba - by - lon. now.
Coda
A♭ E♭maj9/G A♭ E♭maj9/G A♭
now, Ba - by - lon, Ba - by - lon,
E♭maj9/G A♭ E♭maj9/G A♭
Ba - by - lon, Ba - by - lon,
E♭maj9/G A♭ E♭maj9/G
Ba - by - lon, ah.
3fr
4fr

Sunburn

Words & Music by
Matthew Bellamy

Vocals Level 3 - Male

make — no———— mis - takes.———

N.C.

And I'll— hide———— from the world——— be - hind a bro - ken frame;————

— and I'll— run———— for ev - er,——— I can't— face———— the shame.————

— And I'll hide———— from the world——— be - hind a— bro - ken frame;————

———— and I'll— run———— for ev - er,——— I can't— face———— the shame.————

—

Grade 7 *Technical Exercises*

In this section, the examiner will ask you to perform the two exercises printed below. You do not need to memorise the exercises (and you may use the book in the exam) but the examiner will be looking for the speed and confidence of your response. The examiner will also give you credit for the level of your musicality in your attention to directions, including phrasing and dynamics.

Exercise 1: Scales Disc 1 Track 14

You will be asked to perform the following scale and arpeggio exercise beginning on any note between **A-D**. You will be asked to give the exercise *legato* or *staccato* and with *crescendo* and *diminuendo* as directed by the examiner.

Exercise 2: Backing Vocals

You should prepare all three parts of the following two backing vocal exercises. The examiner will select the part to be given against the other two parts on a backing track. Two examples will be selected.

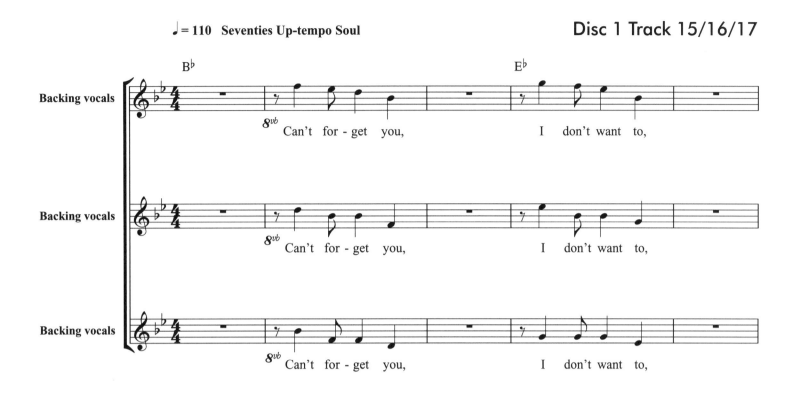

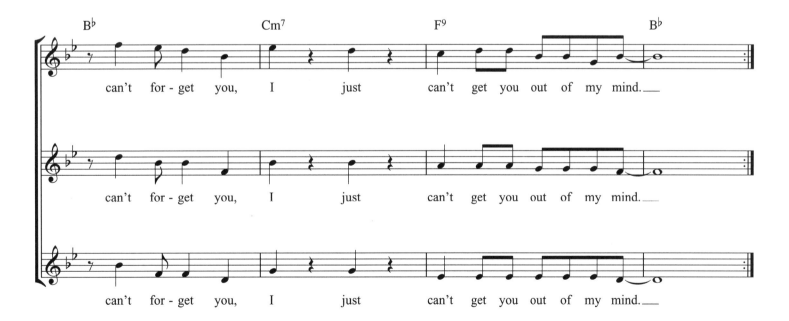

Exercise 4: Backing Vocals (continued)

Disc 1 Track 18/19/20

Supreme

Words & Music by Robbie Williams, Guy Chambers,
Dino Fekaris, Frederick Perren & Francois de Roubaix

Disc 1 Track 21

Vocals Level 3 - Male

Asus⁴ ... A

You must sur - vive._____ When there's no_____

Dm ... B♭maj⁷ ... F

_____ love in town_____ this new cen - tu - ry_____ keeps bring - ing you down._

A ... Dm ... B♭maj⁷

_____ All the pla - ces you have been,_____ try - ing to find_

F ... *To Coda* ⊕ A ... **1.** Dm

_____ a love su - preme,_____ a love su - preme._____

2. Dm ... Gm⁷ ₃fr ... C ... Fmaj⁷

_____

B♭maj⁷ ... Gm⁷ ₃fr ... A ... A⁷

Dm

Spoken: I spy with my lit - tle eye

Verse 2:

Oh, what are you really looking for?
Another partner in your life to abuse and to adore?
Is it lovey dovey stuff
Do you need a bit of rough?
Get on your knees
Yeah, turn down the love songs that you hear
'Cause you can't avoid the sentiment
That echoes in your ear
Saying love will stop the pain
Saying love will kill the fear
Do you believe?
You must believe

When there's no love in town *etc.*

Suspicious Minds

Words & Music
by Francis Zambon

Vocals Level 3 - Male

Mm._____

Yeah_____ yeah.

Outro

We're caught in a trap,_____ I can't walk_ out_

_ be - cause I love_____ you too_____ much_ ba -

- by._____ Why can't you see___
And don't you know I

what you're do - in' to me,_____

when you don't be - lieve_____ the word_____ I say.___

_____ And don't you know I'm

Repeat to fade

I Can't Make You Love Me

Words & Music by
Mike Reid & Allen Shamblin

Disc 1 Track 23

1. Turn down the___ lights,___ turn down___ the bed,_____ turn down these voi - ces___ in - side___ my head.___ Lay down with me,___ tell me no___ lies,___ just hold me close,_ don't pa - tron - ise.___

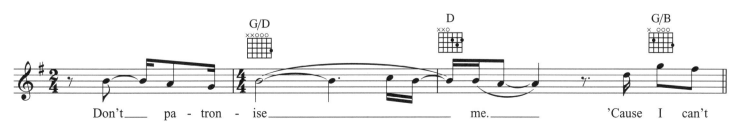

Don't___ pa - tron - ise_____ me.___ 'Cause I can't

Vocals Level 3 - Male

This Year's Love

Words & Music by
David Gray

This year's love, it bet-ter last; _____ hea-ven knows it's high

(Verse 2 see block lyric)

time, _____ I've been wait-ing on my own too_ long. _____

And when you hold me like you do_ it feels_ so right, _ oh now, _

I start to for-get how my heart gets torn when that

(Verse 3 see block lyric)

1.

hurt gets thrown; feel-ing_ like you can't_ go on. _____

2, 3.

_ dream in - side my_ soul, when you kiss me on that mid - night street, sweep me

Vocals Level 3 - Male

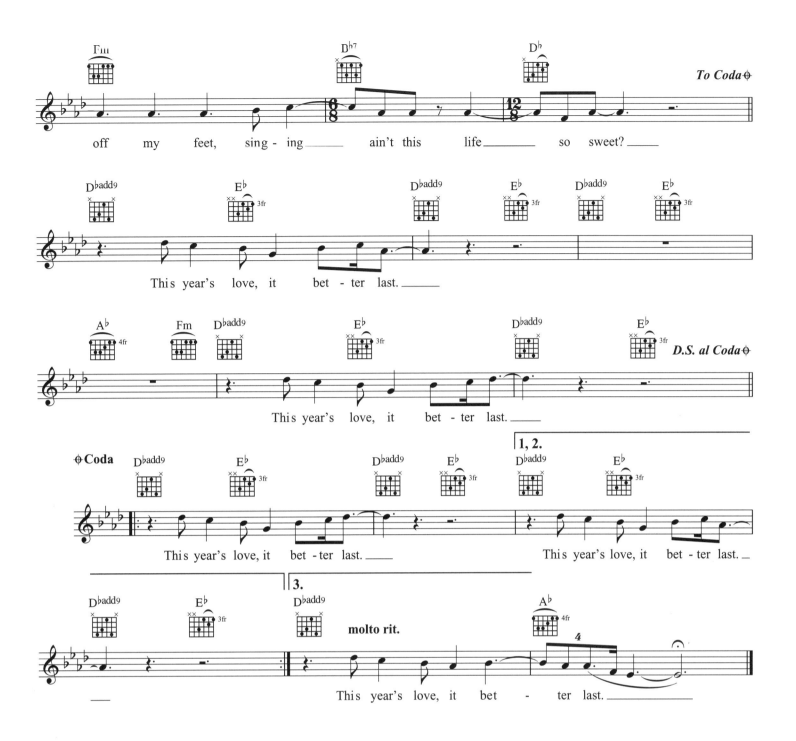

off my feet, sing - ing _____ ain't this life _____ so sweet?

This year's love, it bet - ter last. _____

This year's love, it bet - ter last. _____

D.S. al Coda

Coda

This year's love, it bet - ter last. _____

This year's love, it bet - ter last. _____

molto rit.

This year's love, it bet - ter last. _____

Verse 2:

Turning circles and time again
It cuts like a knife, oh now
If you love me I got to know for sure
'Cause it takes something more this time
Than sweet, sweet lies, oh now
Before I open up my arms and fall
Losing all control
Every dream inside my soul
When you kiss me on that midnight street
Sweep me of my feet
Singing ain't this life so sweet.

Verse 3:

'Cause who's to worry if our hearts get torn
When that hurt gets thrown?
Don't you know this life goes on?
Won't you kiss me on that midnight street
Sweep me off my feet
Singing ain't this life so sweet?

Trouble

Words & Music by Guy Berryman,
Jon Buckland, Will Champion & Chris Martin

1. Oh no, I see a spi-der web is tan-gled up with me. And I lost my head, and thought of all the stu-pid things I'd said.

2. Oh no, what's this? A spi-der web and I'm caught in the mid-dle. So I turned to run, and thought

Vocals Level 3 - Male

_of all___ the stu - pid things___ I'd___ done.

ah,_____ I nev - er meant to cause___ you trou - ble.___

ah,_____ I nev - er meant to do___ you wrong.___

ah,_____ well if I ev - er caused___ you trou - ble,___

To Coda

oh no, I nev - er meant to do___ you harm.___

3. Oh no, I see a spi - der web,___ and it's me in the mid - dle.

I Saw Her Standing There

Words & Music by
John Lennon & Paul McCartney

Vocals Level 3 - Male

Grade 8 *Technical Exercises*

In this section, the examiner will ask you to perform the two exercises printed below. You do not need to memorise the exercises (and you may use the book in the exam) but the examiner will be looking for the speed and confidence of your response. The examiner will also give you credit for the level of your musicality in your attention to directions, including phrasing and dynamics.

Exercise 1: Scales

Disc 2 Track 1

You will be asked to perform the following scale and arpeggio exercise beginning on any note between **A-D**. You will be asked to give the exercise *legato* or *staccato* and with *crescendo* and *diminuendo* as directed by the examiner

Exercise 2: Backing Vocals

You should prepare all three parts of the following two backing vocal exercises. The examiner will select the part to be given against the other two parts on a backing track. Two examples will be selected.

Disc 2 Track 2/3/4

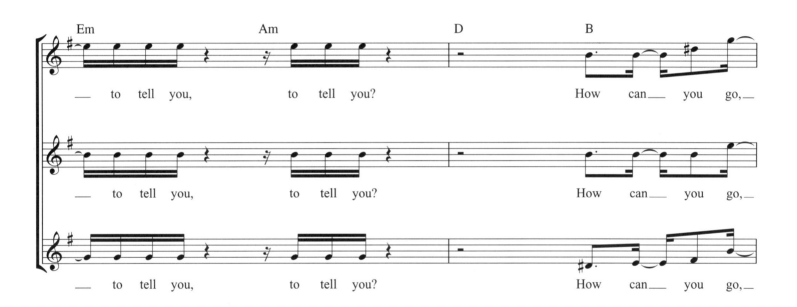

All Right Now

Words & Music by
Paul Rodgers & Andy Fraser

Vocals Level 3 - Male

Stan

Words & Music by Marshall Mathers,
Dido Armstrong & Paul Herman

Chorus (female vocals):

(repeat)

Dear Slim, I wrote you but you still ain't callin'
I left my cell, my pager, and my home phone at the bottom
I sent two letters back in autumn
You must not have got 'em
It probably was a problem at the post office or somethin'.

Sometimes I scribble addresses too sloppy when I jot 'em
But anyways, fuck it, what's been up man, how's your daughter?
My girlfriend's pregnant too, I'm 'bout to be a father
If I have a daughter, guess what I'm-a call her?
I'm-a name her Bonnie.

I read about your uncle Ronnie too, I'm sorry
I had a friend kill himself over some bitch who didn't want him.
I know you probably hear this every day
But I'm your biggest fan.
I even got the underground shit that you did with Scam.

I got a room full of your posters and your pictures, man.
I like the shit you did with Ruckus too, that shit was fat.
Anyways, I hope you get this man
Hit me back, just to chat
Truly yours, your biggest fan, this is Stan.

Chorus:

Dear Slim, you still ain't called or wrote, I hope you have a chance
I ain't mad, I just think it's fucked up you don't answer fans.
If you didn't wanna talk to me outside the concert, you didn't have to.
But you could have signed an autograph for Matthew.
That's my little brother, man. He's only 6 years old.
We waited in the blistering cold for you for 4 hours and you just said no.
That's pretty shitty man, you're like his fuckin' idol
He wants to be just like you man, he likes you more than I do.

I ain't that mad though, I just don't like being lied to.
Remember when we met in Denver, you said if I write to you
You would write back. See, I'm just like you in a way.
I never knew my father neither.
He used to always cheat on my mom and beat her.

I can relate to what you're sayin' in your songs.
So when I have a shitty day, I drift away and put 'em on.
'Cause I don't really got shit else, so that shit helps when I'm depressed.
I even got a tattoo with your name across the chest.

Sometimes I even cut myself to see how much it bleeds.
It's like adrenaline. The pain is such a sudden rush for me.
See, everything you say is real, and I respect you 'cause you tell it.
My girlfriend's jealous 'cause I talk about you 24/7.
But she don't know you like I know you, Slim, no one does.
She don't know what it was like for people like us growing up.
You've gotta call me man. I'll be the biggest fan you'll ever lose.
Sincerely yours, Stan.
PS: We should be together too.

Chorus:

Dear Mr. 'I'm too good to call or write my fans.'
This'll be the last package I ever send your ass.
It's been six months and still no word. I don't deserve it?
I know you got my last two letters, I wrote the addresses on 'em perfect.

So this is my cassette I'm sending you. I hope you hear it.
I'm in the car right now. I'm doing 90 on the freeway.
Hey Slim, "I drank a fifth of vodka, ya dare me to drive?"
You know that song by Phil Collins from 'The Air In The Night'?
About that guy who could have saved that other guy from drowning?
But didn't? Then Phil saw it all then at his show he found him?
That's kinda how this is. You could have rescued me from drowning.
Now it's too late. I'm on a thousand downers now. I'm drowsy.

And all I wanted was a lousy letter or a call.
I hope you know I ripped all o' your pictures off the wall.
I love you Slim, we could have been together. Think about it.
You ruined it now, I hope you can't sleep and you dream about it.
And when you dream, I hope you can't sleep and you scream about it.
I hope your conscience eats at you and you can't breathe without me.
See Slim, [screaming] Shut up bitch! I'm trying to talk!
Hey Slim, that's my girlfriend screaming in the trunk.
But I didn't slit her throat, I just tied her up,
See I ain't like you. 'Cause if she suffocates, she'll suffer more
And then she'll die too.
Well, gotta go, I'm almost at the bridge now.
Oh shit, I forgot, how am I supposed to send this shit out?
[Car crashes, splashes into water]

Chorus:

Dear Stan, I meant to write you sooner, but I've just been busy.
You said your girlfriend's pregnant now, how far along is she?
Look, I'm really flattered you would call your daughter that.
And here's an autograph for your brother: I wrote it on your Starter cap.

I'm sorry I didn't see you at the show, I must have missed you.
Don't think I did that shit intentionally, just to diss you.
And what's this shit you said about you like to cut your wrists too?
I say that shit just clownin' dawg, c'mon, how fucked up is you?
You got some issues, Stan, I think you need some counsellin'
To help your ass from bouncin' off the walls when you get down some.

And what's this shit about us meant to be together?
That type of shit'll make me not want us to meet each other.
I really think you and your girlfriend need each other
Or maybe you just need to treat her better.
I hope you get to read this letter.
I just hope it reaches you in time.
Before you hurt yourself, I think that you'd be doin' just fine
If you'd relax a little, I'm glad I inspire you, but Stan
Why are you so mad? Try to understand that I do want you as a fan.
I just don't want you to do some crazy shit.
I seen this one shit on the news a couple weeks ago that made me sick.
Some dude was drunk and drove his car over a bridge
And had his girlfriend in the trunk and she was pregnant with his kid.
And in the car they found a tape but it didn't say who it was to.
Come to think about it... his name was... it was you.

Damn!

If I Ever Lose My Faith In You

Words & Music by Sting

Disc 2 Track 10

Vocals Level 3 - Male

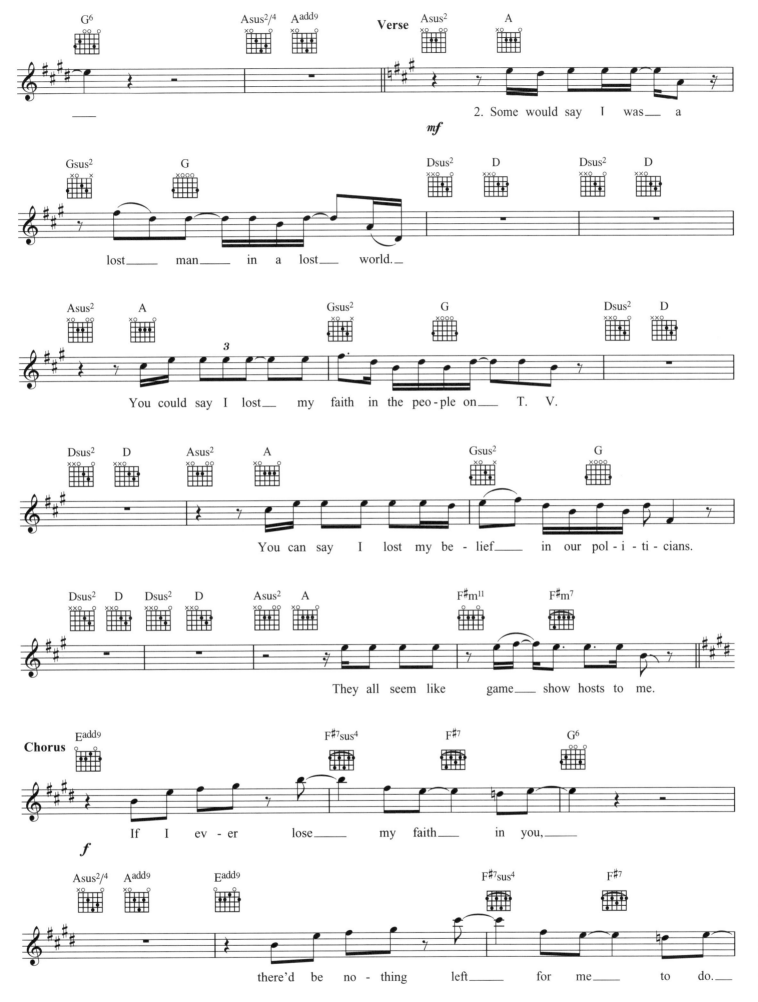

Bridge

I could be lost in - side their lies with - out a trace,

but ev - 'ry time I close my eyes I see your face.

Verse

3. Nev - er saw no mir - a - cle of sci - ence

that did - n't go from a, a bless - ing to a curse.

Nev - er saw no mil - i - tary sol - u - tion

that did - n't al - ways

end up as some-thing worse, but   let me say this first:___

Chorus

If I ev - er   lose___ my faith___ in you,___ if I ev - er   lose___

___ my faith___ in you   there'd be no - thing   left___ for me___ to do,___

___ there'd be no - thing   left___ for me___ to do.___

___ If I ev - er   lose___ my faith,___   if I ev - er   lose___

___ my faith, ___   if I ev - er   lose___ my faith, ___

if I ev - er   lose___ my faith,___   in you.___

Outro

Repeat ad lib to fade

N.C.

mf

If You're Not The One

Words & Music by
Daniel Bedingfield

1. If you're not the one____ then why does____ my soul____ feel____ glad____
(2.) I don't need you____ then why am____ I cry - ing____ on____

____ to - day?____ If you're not the one____ then why does____ my hand____ fit yours____
____ my bed?____ If I don't need you____ then why does____ your name____ re - sound____

____ this way?____ If you are not mine____ then why does____ your heart____ re - turn____
____ in my head?____ If you're not for me____ then why does____ this dis - tance____ maim____

____ my call?____ If you are not mine____ would I have____ the strength____ to stand____
____ my life?____ If you're not for me____ then why do____ I dream____ of you____

____ at all?____ I nev - er know what the fu - ture brings,____ but I
____ as my wife?____ I don't know why you're so far____ a - way,____ but I

know you're here with me now.____ We'll make it through____ and I hope____ you are____ the one____ I
know that this much is true,____ we'll make it through____ and I hope____ you are____ the one____ I

share my____ life with.____
share my____ life with.____

1. I don't wan - na run a - way____ but I____

Repeat to fade

Angels

Words & Music by
Robbie Williams & Guy Chambers

Vocals Level 3 - Male

-tion whe-ther I'm right or wrong. And down the wa-ter-fall___

___ wher-ev-er it___ may take___ me, I know that life___ won't break___

___ me___ when I come___ to call, she won't for-sake___ me,___

I'm lov-ing an-gels in-stead. When I'm feel-ing weak___ and my pain___

___ walks down___ a one-way street, I look a-bove

and I know___ I'll al-ways be blessed___ with love.___

And as the feel-ing grows,___ she brings flesh to my bones and

The Guru's Guide To Level 3 *Male Vocals*

Supplementary Material

Rockschool recommends the following songs in addition to the repertoire printed in this book. The list below shows the songs arranged by grade along with the publications in which they may be found.

Grade 6

Wanted Dead Or Alive	*Play Guitar With Bon Jovi - Early Years*	AM971256
I Knew You Were Waiting (For Me)	*You're The Voice*	IMP9007A
You're In My Heart	*In Session With Rod Stewart*	IMP6607A
When A Man Loves A Woman	*Sing & Party With Tear-jerkers*	IMP9803A
Don't Let The Sun Go Down On Me	*Essential Audition Songs: Pop Ballads*	IMP9776A
Roxanne	*Play Guitar With The Police*	AM960993

Grade 7

Careless Whisper	*You're The Voice: George Michael*	IMP9007A
Hello	*Sing & Party With Tear-jerkers*	IMP9803A
Reet Petite	*Audition Songs For Male Singers 3*	AM972400

Grade 8

Freedom '90	*You're The Voice: George Michael*	IMP9007A
'97 Bonnie And Clyde	*Rap With Eminem*	AM972510
The Real Slim Shady	*Rap With Eminem*	AM972510
My Name Is	*Rap With Eminem*	AM972510

Warm Up

It is important that you prepare for the exam by warming up your voice properly. You should ensure that you arrive at the exam centre within plenty of time to do this. We have arranged the elements of the grade exam such that the performances come at the end. The backing tracks and/or accompaniment are always variable in volume and you should always tell the examiner if you feel that you are straining to be heard.

Free Choice Pieces

In grade exams you are allowed to perform one song not specified in this book. This may be a hit from the chart or a song composed by yourself. In performance certificate exams you are allowed to perform up to two songs not specified in this book.

If you wish to find out whether a free choice piece song is appropriate for the grade, you may either contact Rockschool and submit the song for adjudication, or look on our website www.rockschool.co.uk and consult the free choice piece criteria.

Marking Schemes

The table below shows the marking schemes for grad exams and performance certificates. All Rockschool exams are marked out of 100 and the pass mark for a grade exam is 65% and for a performance certificate is 70%.

Grade Exam

Element	Pass	Merit	Distinction
Technical Exercises	6 out of 10	7 out of 10	8 out of 10
General Musicianship Questions	3 out of 5	4 out of 5	5 out of 5
Aural Tests	6 out of 10	7 out of 10	8 out of 10
Quick Study Piece	11 out of 15	12 out of 15	13 out of 15
Piece 1	13 out of 20	15 out of 20	17 out of 20
Piece 2	13 out of 20	15 out of 20	17 out of 20
Piece 3	13 out of 20	15 out of 20	17 out of 20

Performance Certificate

Element	Pass	Merit	Distinction
Piece 1	14 out of 20	16 out of 20	18 out of 20
Piece 2	14 out of 20	16 out of 20	18 out of 20
Piece 3	14 out of 20	16 out of 20	18 out of 20
Piece 4	14 out of 20	16 out of 20	18 out of 20
Piece 5	14 out of 20	16 out of 20	18 out of 20

Examination Criteria

Rockschool examiners assess all examinations according to strict guidelines. Copies of these for vocals can be found on the website www.rockschool.co.uk or direct from our offices. Please ring **020 8332 6303** for further details.

Exam Regulations

Entering a Rockschool exam is easy. Please read through the instructions on the back of the entry form accompanying this book carefully, before filling it in. Information on current fees can be obtained by ringing Rockschool on **020 8332 6303** or by logging on to the website www.rockschool.co.uk.